LARRY BENDECO JOHANNES VON SLOOP

A STORY BY LARRY V.
ILLUSTRATED BY MARK K.

A LONG TIME AGO...

in a town not **TOO** far from here,

there lived two **BROTHERS**.

One brother was called

LARRY
BENDECO
JOHANNES
VON SLOOP.

The other brother was called
Bob.

They were **BROTHERS**,
and therefore shared the same **LAST NAME**,
but when anyone tried to call
Bob,
Bob **BENDECO JOHANNES VON SLOOP**,
Bob would always say,
"Please, call me **Bob**."

And if someone happened to say,
"Oh, and you must be his brother, LARRY."

LARRY
BENDECO
JOHANNES
VON SLOOP

would always say, "Please, call me

LARRY
BENDECO
JOHANNES
VON SLOOP ."

AS YOU MIGHT IMAGINE, the way these two **BROTHERS** felt about their **NAMES** was very similar to how they felt about **MANY, MANY** things.

LARRY

BENDECO

JOHANNES

VON SLOOP

liked things formal,
and fancy,
and felt that made them
SPECIAL.

LARRY BENDECO JOHANNES VON SLOOP

and **Bob**
were both really
GREAT bakers.
AWESOME bakers.
FANTABULOUS bakers.
They could bake just about **ANYTHING**.
And after **YEARS** of practice
they were ready to open a bakery.

Bob said to

LARRY

BENDECO

JOHANNES

VON SLOOP

"Hey, **LARRY**

BENDECO

JOHANNES

VON SLOOP,
would you like
to open a bakery
with me?"

But **LARRY**

BENDECO

JOHANNES

VON SLOOP

thought **Bob**'s baking was **SIMPLE**,
and **PLAIN**, and he told him so.

So, the two **BROTHERS** decided they
would **EACH** open their **OWN** bakeries.

When **LARRY BENDECO JOHANNES VON SLOOP** opened **HIS** bakery, he decided he would only bake the **FINEST** of cakes. **ELABORATE** cakes. **EYE-POPPING** cakes. Very **FANCY SHMANCY** cakes. They would have **DECORATIONS** that were like **ART**. People would comment that they were like the **FINEST** paintings they had **EVER** seen. **UNFORTUNATELY,** they tasted like paintings, too!

"I don't **CARE** how they **TASTE**,"
LARRY BENDECO JOHANNES VON SLOOP
would say,
"I want people to be
IMPRESSED
with how they
LOOK!"

When **Bob** opened **HIS** bakery, he decided to make **SIMPLE** breads and **COOKIES**.

They were **DELICIOUS**.

One day,
a **FIRE** broke out in

Bob's kitchen.

"Oh, **SHOOT** !"

thought Bob.

LUCKILY, a customer saw the **FIRE,** and they quickly **RUSHED** to find **HELP.**

"Thanks," said the **DISPATCHER,** who immediately connected to the **FIRE** department. "Go to **Bob**'s! There is a **FIRE**!"

"**HELP**! There's a **FIRE** at **Bob**'s!" she said.

A **SHOPKEEPER** nearby heard the cry and immediately dialed **911**.

"**HELP**! There's a **FIRE** at **Bob**'s!" they yelled.

"A **FIRE** at **Bob's**?"
responded the **CHIEF**,
"We're **ON** it!"

"All **HANDS** on deck!
We've got a **FIRE** at **Bob's**!"
called the **CHIEF**.
And the **FIREMEN**
jumped into action.

In **VERY** short order,
they had
the **FIRE** out
at the bakery.

"**Thanks!**" said **Bob**.

A few days later,
a **FIRE** broke out in
LARRY
BENDECO
JOHANNES
VON SLOOP's
kitchen.

"Oh, **SHOOT**!" thought
LARRY
BENDECO
JOHANNES
VON SLOOP.

LUCKILY, a customer saw the **FIRE**, and they quickly **RUSHED** to find **HELP**.

"I said: There's a **FIRE** at **LARRY BENDECO JOHANNES VON SLOOP**'s!"

"**PARDON**?" asked the **DISPATCHER**.

"**HELP**! There's a **FIRE** at **LARRY BENDECO JOHANNES VON SLOOP**'s!" she said.

A **SHOPKEEPER** nearby heard the cry and immediately dialed **911**.

"**HELP**! There's a **FIRE** at **LARRY BENDECO JOHANNES VON SLOOP**'s!" they yelled.

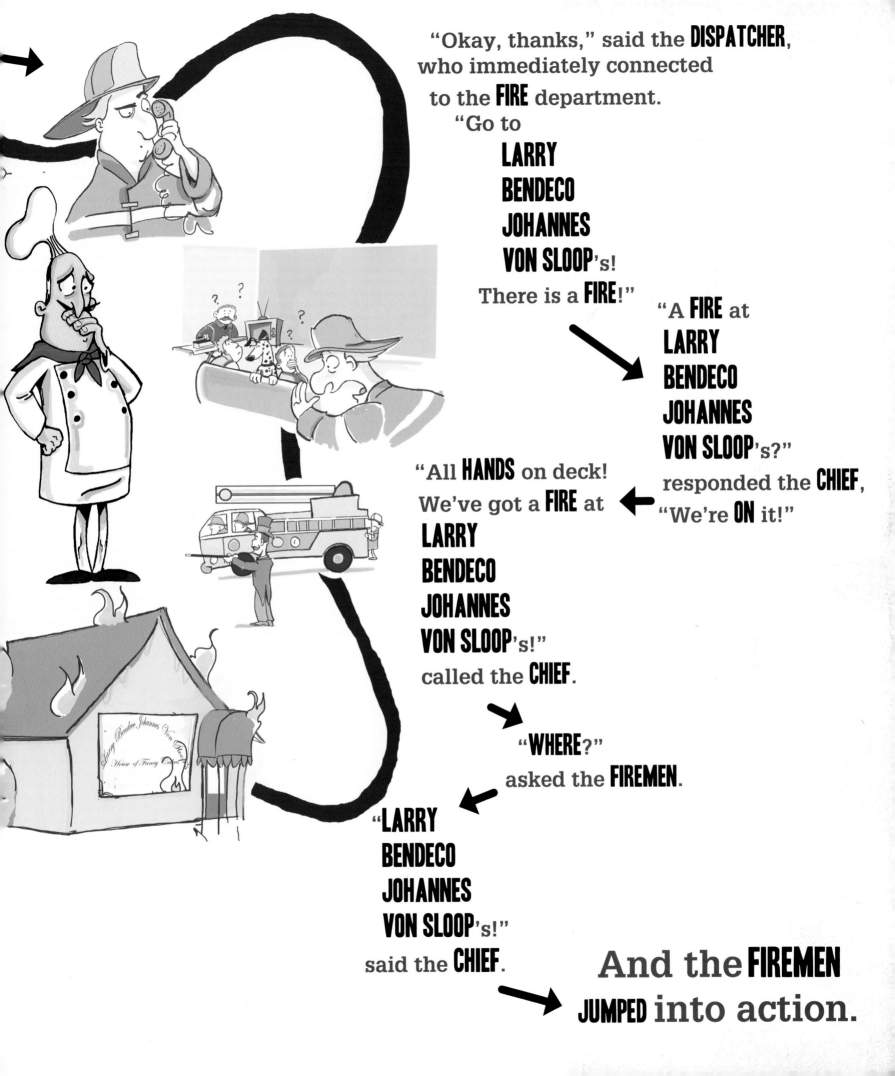

"Okay, thanks," said the **DISPATCHER**, who immediately connected to the **FIRE** department.
"Go to **LARRY BENDECO JOHANNES VON SLOOP**'s! There is a **FIRE**!"

"A **FIRE** at **LARRY BENDECO JOHANNES VON SLOOP**'s?" responded the **CHIEF**, "We're **ON** it!"

"All **HANDS** on deck! We've got a **FIRE** at **LARRY BENDECO JOHANNES VON SLOOP**'s!" called the **CHIEF**.

"**WHERE**?" asked the **FIREMEN**.

"**LARRY BENDECO JOHANNES VON SLOOP**'s!" said the **CHIEF**.

And the **FIREMEN** **JUMPED** into action.

As you can IMAGINE,
all the
LARRY
BENDECO
JOHANNES
VON SLOOPs
had SLOWED things down quite a BIT,
so when they got to the BAKERY,
it was TOO late.

"SHOOT!" said
LARRY
BENDECO
JOHANNES
VON SLOOP.

LOSING his bakery got

LARRY
BENDECO
JOHANNES
VON SLOOP
thinking.

It made him **THINK**
about why his **BROTHER'S** bakery
was **SAVED** and his was **NOT**.
It made him think
about a **LOT** of things.

"Maybe **FANCY** and **FORMAL**
is not so **SPECIAL**,
and maybe **SIMPLE** and **FRIENDLY**
is not so **PLAIN**,"
he thought.

When **Bob** **SAW** what had happened, he said to

LARRY BENDECO JOHANNES VON SLOOP,

"Hey, **LARRY BENDECO JOHANNES VON SLOOP**, would you like to come work with **ME** in my **BAKERY**?"

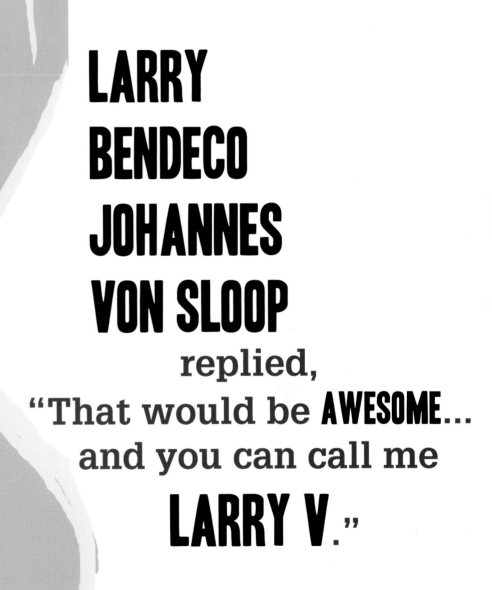

LARRY BENDECO JOHANNES VON SLOOP replied, "That would be **AWESOME...** and you can call me **LARRY V**."

Now the
TWO brothers
work **HAPPILY** away
in their **BAKERY**
making **DELICIOUS**
BREADS and **COOKIES**.
It is **SIMPLE**,
and **FRIENDLY**,
and **NICE**.

Every **ONCE** in a while,
LARRY V.
takes **TIME** out
from his not-so-**BUSY** day
to **SIT**
and **WRITE** stories.

One day he sat down
and wrote **THIS** one.